Inspired by the life of Mr. James Harold Floyd,
an unflagging optimist.

Momma and Daddy,

Thank you for feeding my constant curiosity and filling my life with your unwavering and unconditional love.

Chuckie,

Thank you for being on this adventure with me. Here's to faith and love. I am excited about fulfilling many more dreams with you.

Always,
Sherri

www.mascotbooks.com

Is My Cup Empty?

©2014 Sherri Graves Smith. All Rights Reserved. No part of this publication may be reproduced, stored in a retrieval system or transmitted in any form by any means electronic, mechanical, or photocopying, recording or otherwise without the permission of the author.

For more information, please contact:
Mascot Books
560 Herndon Parkway #120
Herndon, VA 20170
info@mascotbooks.com

CPSIA Code: PRT0215B
ISBN-13: 978-1-62086-920-8

Printed in the United States

Is My Cup EMPTY?

Sherri Graves Smith

illustrated by **Damon Danielson**

If your cup is empty, it can still be filled

with water, milk, or juice that's chilled.

If your plate is empty, try more healthy foods

like chicken and veggies if you're in the mood.

If your day feels empty, then fill it with fun!
Ride bikes, play games, or just walk in the sun.

If your notebook's new and the pages are bare,
write a letter or poem, or put drawings there.

If your piggy bank has just two pennies and a dime,

do some chores and make money with your time!

If your toy box is empty, your room filled with clutter, pick up your toys! That would really help your mother.

If your basket is empty, here's a little trick:
Fill it with goodies and visit someone sick.

If Grandma's lap is empty and she needs love, climb right up on it to give her kisses and a hug!

If the seat next to you is empty at school,
invite someone to sit and talk. Being nice is cool!

If your life's feeling empty—you haven't a friend—
be thoughtful and just let new friendships begin.

If your head's feeling empty, how about a book?
Books hold adventures. Go on and take a look!

If your bowl is empty, here's something to do:
Make popcorn to share with a good friend or two.

If both hands are empty, just offer some help.
Put things in the trash and clean up after yourself.

If the scoreboard is empty—your team hasn't scored—

just keep right on playing. Who knows what's in store!

If you're feeling down and things didn't go your way,

do something thoughtful and help someone today.

If you're feeling sad and your house seems empty,
spend time with your pets, best friends, or family.

If your own heart is empty, filling it takes little skill.
Just find someone to love today, then watch it fill!

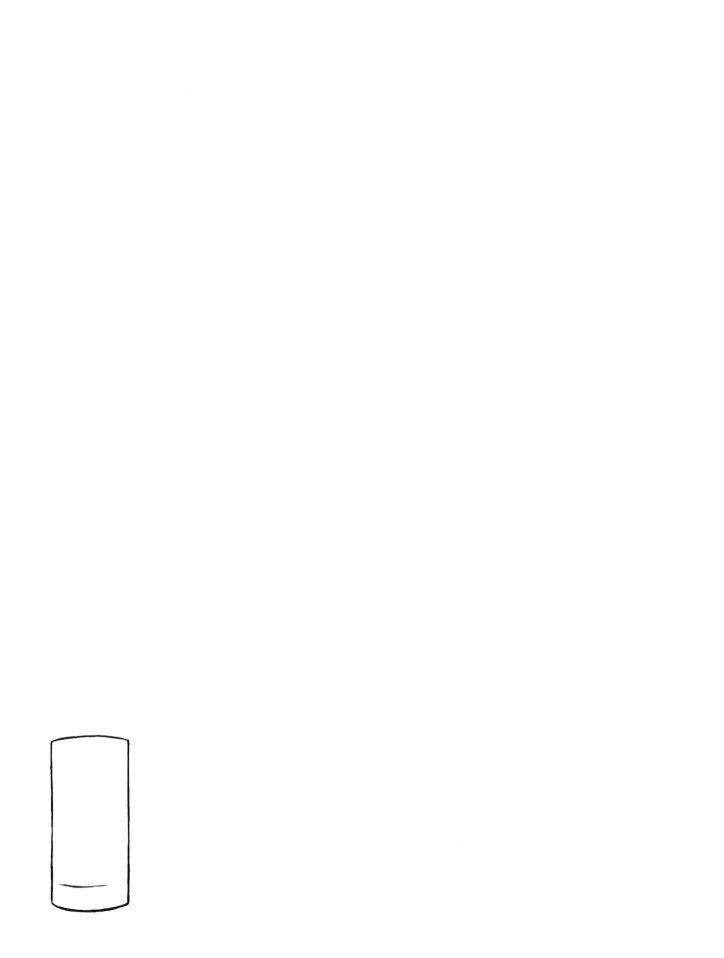

Check out your favorite college mascot in Sherri's other children's book series, Game Day Rules!

Dear Reader,

Welcome to the *Lil' Sherri* series. My cherished older sister, Lisa, called me Lil' Sherri when I was a little girl. This character is based on my first grade school picture.

The lessons instilled in my heart as a child have influenced my life profoundly. My mission is to write books that plant seeds of optimism, gratitude, hope, kindness, and love. Thanks to my loving parents, family, friends, teachers, and the community of Tuscumbia, Alabama, my childhood was full of these beautiful seeds being planted in my heart. They have grown and blossomed over the years and I want to share this bountiful, beautiful garden with you.

I am honored and grateful that you have allowed Lil' Sherri and her friends to share this message with you.

Hugs,
Sherri

P.S. For you adults, I hope you enjoy this message too. Sometimes, we have to keep it simple in order to remind ourselves about this gift of life!

Many things may seem empty as you live this life.
But the way you fill them turns darkness to light.